THE U.K. GREAT WHITE SHARK ENIGMA

RICHARD PEIRCE

Published by:
Shark Cornwall Publishing, Passingham House, Crooklets,
Bude, Cornwall, EX23 8NE.

First published: 2016

© Richard Peirce, Shark Cornwall Publishing.

ISBN no. 978-0-9558694-7-1
Photographs: As indicated
Design and Artwork: SR Print Management
Printed and bound in England by
SR Print Management Limited, Newmarket 2, Centrix@Keys,
Keys Park Road, Hednesford, Staffordshire WS12 2HA

SOON TO BE PUBLISHED BY THE SAME AUTHOR
"Giant Steps" – Book
*"Westcountry Witches, Wizards, Warlocks,
Black Magic & Satanism"* – Book
"The Long Swim" – Book

OTHER PRODUCTS
"Sharks in British Seas" – Book (2008/2011)
"Sharks in British Seas" – DVD (2009)
"Sharks off Cornwall and Devon" – Book (2009)
"Shark Attack Britain" – DVD (2010)
"Pirates of Devon & Cornwall" – Book (2010/11/14)
"Execution Sites of Devon & Cornwall" – Book (2013)
"The Poacher's Moon" – Book (2013/2014)

All books and DVD's can be bought through our website –
www.peirceshark.com

INTRODUCTION

I suspect there are not many people who, like me, would regard a confirmed sighting of a Great White Shark in UK waters as good news! However although a confirmed sighting will be headline news when and if it occurs, I don't believe it is really 'new' news. As this short book will establish there is no reason why we don't have Great White Sharks in our waters, and my belief is that we have had occasional Great White vagrant visitors for many many years.

This book lists some of the more credible reports of Great Whites in our waters, and examines the enigma of why we don't have a permanent population when our marine conditions would appear to be ideal in many ways.

For anyone who may be alarmed at the possibility of Great Whites in British seas let me make a few points. There is no record of a 'real' shark attack in our waters in recent times. If Great Whites do visit us, the visits are very few and far between and may well have been occurring for a very long time. Overfishing has greatly decreased the Great White population and looks set to continue to do so, therefore the chances of vagrant visitors are probably reducing. When and if a Great White Shark is confirmed in UK waters don't get panicked by alarmist headlines in the tabloids, celebrate the addition of a wonderful, beautiful, and awesome creature to our list of marine fauna.

Richard Peirce

DEDICATION

This book is dedicated to one of the most misunderstood animals on the planet – the Great White Shark.

THANKS & ACKNOWLEDGEMENTS

I wish to thank the following for either providing source material, or for their direct personal contribution/s.

Brian Bate
Phil Britts
George Carter
Nick Fletcher
Dr. Simon Greenstreet
Monty Halls
Philip Harding
Sally Houseago
James Innes
Jody MacNeil
John Reynolds
Lalo Saidy
The Shark Trust
Lizzy & Simon Sharp
Brenda du Toit
Alison Towner
David Turner
Mike Turner
Dr. Charlie Underwood
Paul Vincent
John Watson

and a special thank you to Harry Stone for very kindly allowing us to use some of his excellent Great White Shark images.

SECTIONS

Dedication, Thanks & Acknowledgements iv

Section One

The Great White Shark 3

Section Two

The enigma 7

Section Three

Sightings and events 13

Section Four

Conclusions and the future 47

No shark attracts human attention like the Great White.

© Harry Stone

SECTION ONE

GREAT WHITE SHARK

Sharks both terrify and fascinate humans, and of all sharks the Great White in particular attracts our attention. Legions of fans all over the world are captivated by this iconic creature. Beautiful, majestic, sleek, exciting, deadly, powerful, charismatic, and others are all adjectives often used to describe this apex predator.

The Great White has always been the king or queen of sharks and the most feared, and when the film Jaws was released it confirmed the Great White's position.

Great Whites are distributed throughout the world's temperate seas; however they are semi-warm blooded, and can regulate their body temperatures, which increases their range into sub-tropical and cold oceans.

Great Whites are now listed by the International Union for Conservation & Nature as 'Vulnerable'. Although populations are now seriously depleted due to over fishing, they still exist in various hotspots among which are South Australia, California and

South Africa. Perhaps the world's best known Great White viewing area is around South Africa's Dyer Island, offshore from Gansbaai.

This small island is separated from a long large rocky outcrop called Geyser Rock by a shallow channel known as Shark Alley.

Geyser Rock is home to up to 60,000 Cape Fur Seals which are a favourite prey species for Great Whites. Every year the colony produces 10,000 – 12,000 pups of which only a small percentage survive to adulthood.

Geyser Rock is home to up to 60,000 Cape Fur Seals. © Richard Peirce.

Most pups die of other causes, but predation by Great Whites is a significant contributor to the high mortality rate.

Great Whites are just over a metre long when born, and females have been recorded measuring up to 6 metres. They are distinguished by their pure white underbelly and their large, flat, triangular teeth. The colour change from a greyish-black topside to white underside is a marked serrated line with an immediate colour change – no bleeding together of colours.

Great White females may not be sexually mature until they are 20 years old, and they produce litters of between two and thirteen pups every two or three years following a twelve month gestation period. It is thought that males aren't sexually mature until they are at least ten years old, and this low reproduction rate makes the species particularly vulnerable to over-fishing. Their diet is varied and ranges from small fishes to large marine mammals. These sharks are inquisitive and intelligent and their behaviour involves complex social interactions. They are highly efficient hunters and many people will have seen photographs showing them breaching to attack seals.

Although Great Whites are often found close inshore they are known to undertake ocean migrations. On the 7th November 2003 a Great White was tagged near Dyer Island, and the tag stayed on until 28th February 2004. It was pre-set to pop off after three months, and researchers were shocked and delighted when it popped up off the western Australian coast near the Ningaloo Reef. The female Great White was instantly world famous as this event was the longest recorded journey yet undertaken by a Great White, and the first scientific proof of an inter-continental migration by this species. The shark was later named Nicole after the actress Nicole Kidman who is a committed shark enthusiast. She cemented her position as an ocean traveller when 9 months later in August 2004 she re-appeared in Gansbaai. She had covered a total of at least 22,000 kms, and her journey ensured her place in history. There are many people who believe we get Great Whites in British waters, and for them Nicole's journey underlined how possible it is that these sharks could reach British shores.

Enthusiasts can view Great Whites from the safety of cages. © Harry Stone.

SECTION TWO

THE ENIGMA

Why isn't the Great White Shark a permanent resident in British waters? Conditions are broadly similar to those where large resident populations exist in Africa, Australia, and California. The nearest confirmed Great White Shark to our waters was a female captured in 1977 in the northern Bay of Biscay off La Rochelle – 168 nautical miles from Land's End. Nicole's epic journey from South Africa to Western Australia emphatically shows that 168 miles is no distance for these sharks.

Fishermen's stories are renowned for their colour and exaggeration. By the mid 1990's, I realised that I was continually hearing stories of large, powerful, unidentified sharks in UK waters. Could some of them be Great Whites? There was no reason why not, so I started logging each report.

My record keeping has not included all the reports I have received, because some claimed sightings were so ludicrous they weren't worth noting or considering further. However, from 1996 until the time of writing I can certainly say that I have heard of nearly 100 possible Great White Shark encounters. Most of the sightings involved Basking Sharks or Porbeagles, however nine of those investigated remain credible as Great Whites after further examination. I am not saying that these nine incidents involved Great Whites, but the descriptions certainly fit.

So do these sharks visit our shores? The jury is out and will remain so until firm proof exists – a carcass, tooth, tissue sample, photograph or some other conclusive evidence.

The real question is not whether we get Great Whites in our waters, but why we don't have a resident population, or regular visitors? As I have said marine conditions are similar to those found in Great White hotspots, and seal colonies around the British Isles would provide a preferred food source. The Monach Islands off North Uist in Scotland's Outer Hebrides are home to approximately 35,000 seals which are at their highest numbers in the autumn. This is the second largest Grey Seal colony in the world, and every year in late September/early October 8,000 – 9,000 pups are born. Grey Seals are not the only species present in these waters as Common Seals are spread throughout the islands. Common Seals give birth in June and July and often pup in the intertidal zone.

The UK population of Common Seals is estimated at 50,000 – 60,000 individuals and 85% occur in Scotland. The combined population of seals, Grey and Common in the area of North Uist is around 40,000. It really is an enigma why Great White Sharks aren't regular visitors to such an abundant food source.

From the tip of Cornwall to the Hebrides the water temperatures are within the tolerance range of the Great White Shark. The water temperatures are right, the food source is plentiful, and we have a confirmed record of a Great White Shark less than 170 nautical miles from the Cornish coast.

I am convinced that we get the occasional vagrant visitor, and that it is only a matter of time before one of these visits produces a proven record. When this happens this book will be overtaken by events which, from an author's and a publishing point of view will be disappointing, but on all other levels it will, for me, be a red letter day, a real cause for celebration.

The Outer Hebrides has a large population of Grey & Common Seals. © Richard Peirce.

This is the form I use to record possible Great White Shark sightings/encounters.

Claimed Great White Shark sightings/encounters in UK waters.

Date _____

Location _____

Lat/Long _____

Diving/Snorkeling/from boat/or land _____

Sea State _____

Weather conditions _____

Surface visibility _____

In water visibility _____

No. of sharks seen _____

Size estimate (total length) _____

Girth estimate (widest point) _____

Distinguishing features (scars/tags etc. _____

Dorsal surface colour _____

Ventral surface colour _____

Gills – size/position _____

Snout/nose shape (pointed, bulbous, rounded) _____

Size of dorsal fin _____

Shape of dorsal fin (triangular, rounded tip, pointed tip) _____

Dorsal/Ventral colour separation

(bleeding in or separate) _____

Eye (large, small, colour) _____

Bait fish present? _____

General fish activity _____

Unusual fish activity _____

Seals present? _____

Other witnesses (details)_____

_____

Has witness seen sharks before if so what?_____

_____

If Great White Sharks seen before, where? _____

Basking Shark activity in the area? _____

General description of animal in question _____

_____

Description of behaviour _____

_____

_____

Distance from witness to shark _____

Length of time shark was in sight_____

Age of witness_____

Sex of witness_____

Witness profession or occupation _____

Witness name and address _____

_____

_____

General comments by witness _____

General comments by recorder _____

Recorder Name _____   Date _____

Recorder Address _____

December 2003
North East
Scotland

July 2003
Near
Ullapool

July 2007
Sound of Harris

July 2005
North Uist

North Cornwall
August 1999
September 1999
July 2002
August 1995

July 1970
Looe

July 1994
Dartmouth

1965
Falmouth

The incidents that remain credible following investigation are clustered in two areas of the British Isles

12

SECTION THREE

SIGHTINGS AND EVENTS

Most of the sightings reports contained in this section fall into the category of those that remain credible following investigation, most but not all!

The following is an extract from a book called 'The Shark Fisherman' by David Turner and is reproduced by kind permission of Little Egret Press and David Turner.

THE FALMOUTH GREAT WHITE: SUMMER 1965

"Of all the stories told of big sharks caught off Falmouth none was more intriguing than the following which was often discussed among shark anglers fishing out of Falmouth and beyond.

I wasn't on board on the day of the incident. It was 1965 the year before I fished out of Falmouth, a pity I didn't see it as I could have identified it easily, but in the following years I got to know several of the experienced anglers who were on board including Doug Phillips who hooked it, and skipper Robin Vinnicombe who came very close to boating it. The first I heard of it was in a tackle shop owned by Fred Taylor a respected Oxford Angler. There was another lad in

13

there about my age and he asked if I went shark fishing, I answered in the affirmative. He told me he and his dad spent their summer holidays sharking on board Eddie Lakeman's boat 'Penare' out of Mevagissey. They had just returned from their annual holiday the previous weekend, and he showed me a photograph of a 40lb Blue he had caught. There were large teeth marks on it. "As I was winding it in a big Mako grabbed it. There was also another big Mako hooked off Falmouth last week too, did you hear about that, it was hooked on Robin Vinnicombe's boat Inter Nos", he concluded. I hadn't heard about it but sure enough, when my copy of Angling Times arrived there was a report of 'an 800lb Mako' hooked and lost off Falmouth.

Maybe the attack on the hooked shark off Mevagissey and another incident were coincidental, but they suggested the presence of an unusually large shark in the waters off Cornwall in that summer of 1965. Businessman Harry Dutfield, director of a carpet manufacturing company and a keen shark fisherman had his own boat moored at Falmouth, he was a good friend of Robin and they often talked over the radio whilst out fishing. A couple of days before Doug Phillips hooked his shark, Harry was fishing off the Manacles. For a rubby dubby container Harry used a plastic laundry basket which was hanging over the side of his boat. Robin later relayed the following incident to me. "We were out a couple of days before Doug hooked his shark when Harry Dutfield came over the radio in an excited, almost hysterical voice, 'Inter Nos, Inter Nos, Harry here Rob, a bloody great shark has just come up and eaten the bloody rubby dubby basket,' Harry is not one to get overexcited", Robin said, "but he was that day alright, I'd never heard him like that before".

Although I was not there, I got the following account direct from Doug and Robin, confirmed by Frank Crooks and others also on board that day. After Harry Dutfield's encounter with the large shark anticipation was probably heightened a couple of days later when Doug Phillips reel gave a couple of clicks on the ratchet. A light take is often the characteristic of a large shark, one of the few credible moments in the film *"Jaws"* is when the reel emits a couple of clicks and Quint picks up the rod without the others even noticing it, frequently that is the only indication given on the initial contact with a big fish. Doug waited for the reel to sound again and then reeled the line tight and struck. The hook went home and he told me he could feel it was a big fish right away but surprisingly it came quickly and easily to the boat.

To everyone's amazement within minutes the shark was alongside the boat. Those on board couldn't believe their eyes, even Robin, no stranger to big Makos, was stunned by its size. He later described it to me as being between twelve and fourteen feet long. Maybe he could have gaffed it then, but Robin was no fool and he knew that a fish of that size still had plenty of strength in it, and to try and boat it whilst still fresh would spell trouble, so instead he poked it in the eye with the gaff handle and it took off. Spray soaked most of those on board as line screamed from Doug's reel. Rob fired up' Inter Nos'

Mrs Yallop with her British record Mako in 1971. 6 years after the Falmouth angling incident which some thought was a Mako. © Shark Angling Club.

and started to follow the monster shark.

For the next three hours the shark didn't show itself again, every time Doug regained line, the shark took it back and he was showing signs of fatigue when the shark re-surfaced, but it was still not over. For the next hour and a half the monster fish circled the boat on the surface and often just beyond the reach of the gaffs, which were all set to deal with it. All on board saw and watched it during this time but then – disaster! The line went slack, the 250lb braided stainless steel trace had frayed through on the sharks teeth, and it swam off into the deep leaving many intriguing questions behind. There is little doubt that a very large shark was hooked that day, it was clearly witnessed by around ten people and it doesn't seem credible that, collectively, they would fabricate and maintain such a story independent of each other for years to come. It was originally reported in the angling press as an "800lb Mako" and in occasional conversation merely as "the big shark" and the talk was of the epic battle rather than its unusual size. It was during a conversation some time later with Robin that he told me that the shark was between 12 & 14ft long. My immediate reaction was "Are you sure it wasn't a Great White". He admitted that he had a suspicion that it may have been, but he reported it as a Mako because he didn't think anyone would believe him, and he would become the laughingstock of the fleet without firm evidence.

What was the evidence? The shark was 'Mako shaped', short fins, stocky build, more or less symmetrical tail. To my knowledge no Porbeagle has ever been recorded anywhere near this size so that would narrow the possibilities down to a Mako or a Great White. A Mako is a possibility but further evidence tends to lean towards the shark having been a Great White. Although the shark was clearly visible for more than an hour, including a short period right alongside the boat, no one saw the definitive evidence of the teeth, but the fact that the steel trace was frayed through suggests the teeth were serrated, the Mako has smooth curved needle shaped teeth unlikely to be capable of causing fraying of a steel trace. The final piece of evidence pointing towards a Great White, although again not conclusive, is the way the shark behaved on the line. When hooked, Makos, in by far the majority of cases, leap out of the water, in fact I only know of one caught off Cornwall that didn't jump out of the water and I caught it! This shark fought stubbornly and deep for much of the battle but there were none of the high speed runs associated with a Mako, especially one of this size!!

LOOE, CORNWALL: JULY 1970

John Reynolds, a Looe-based shark angling skipper, had been at sea all day about eight miles offshore with baited lines out and two rubby dubby bags dangling in the water. In that year Porbeagle and Blue Shark numbers were much higher than they are now, so it was unusual that they had not seen one all day. John's theory is that the lack of other sharks might have indicated the presence of a larger predator.

At sometime around 3pm John started to take in his lines and rubby dubby bags in preparation for returning to shore. He was pulling in the stern bag when a large shark appeared only a few feet

Great White Shark spy-hopping. © Richard Peirce.

This is what John Reynolds saw. © Richard Peirce.

behind the boat.

The animal looked straight at John, staying in a head-up position for some seconds before slipping back into the water and disappearing. John saw only the head but his description fits a Great White Shark and it is the only shark commonly known to spy-hop, which is the action of putting its head out of the water. Spy-hopping has rarely been observed in non-baited conditions and may not be natural behaviour. Current opinion suggests it is a response to concentrated scent stimuli at the surface like chum lines, and not an attempt to espy objects above the surface as had been previously thought. Spy-hopping is also practised by some whales but I have never heard of any of our existing shark species doing this.

The incident described by John fits a Great White Shark spy-hopping.

DARTMOUTH, DEVON: JULY 1994

In 1994 Simon and Lizzy Sharp of Dartmouth spent all their spare time in the water. Both were keen spear fishers, divers and snorkelers. On a bright July day in 1994 they left Dartmouth at 4.00 p.m. with a diving party. They anchored in Hope Cove in Torbay, and after the divers had submerged Lizzy went spear fishing while Simon stayed on the boat with their friend Jane.

"After being in the water a few minutes, I was overcome with a sense of unease which only intensified as I got further away from

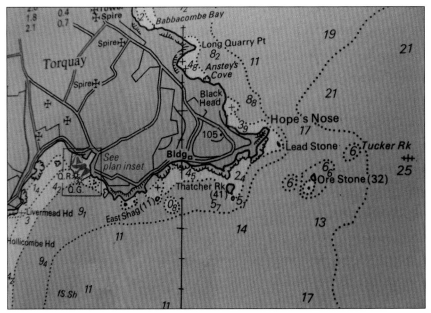

What Simon, Lizzy and Jane saw in Hope Cove precisely fits a Great White Shark.
© *Ordnance Survey.*

the boat. This was unusual as I had never felt uneasy before. The desire

to get out of the water became overwhelming and I couldn't ignore it.

I swum to the boat and got out, much to the surprise of my husband

Simon. As I undid my wetsuit I saw a huge splash to the right of where I

had been. Did you see that?" I asked. Simon said it was probably a bass

jumping, my response was, 'no it was something bigger, much, much

bigger'. We looked in the direction of the splash. A minute or two later, a

seal came out of the water as if it had been tossed in the air, it was followed

by a very large shark which looked as though it had landed on top of it,

there was a lot of tail thrashing and then nothing. We all agree that the

shark was well over 3 metres long. The silence was deafening, you could

have heard a pin drop. We were immediately concerned for the safety of the divers who had actually headed in the opposite direction to me. When they surfaced we urged them to get out of the water a.s.a.p.

As we left the area a fisherman by the name of Matthew Oulds arrived to put his mackerel nets out, Simon told him he didn't think it was a good idea and explained what we had just seen. He brushed it off as 'probably a basking shark' and set his nets. We saw him a few days later, and he said our advice had been right as he lost a large section of net that night."

Witnesses - Simon & Lizzy Sharp & Jane

ST IVES, CORNWALL: AUGUST 1995

The following account was written by Sally Houseago who is convinced that she had a close encounter with a Great White Shark.

"I am credible and not some loony idiot. I have a degree in marine biology and I studied reef ecology in Tanzania. I am a fully qualified diver with the British Sub Aqua Club, and have dived over most of the world for research purposes. I have a keen interest in sharks and have done various work on reef sharks in coastal waters.

I was camping in St. Ives about 15 yrs ago, I was with friends and we decided to go just outside the harbour on jet skis which are available for public rent. The weather was dull and overcast and the water was reflecting this - the visibility was poor, but none of us minded. I was around 25 yrs old at the time and I recall this day vividly. I swapped with my friend from a sit down ski to a stand/kneel ski as I was more confident and enjoyed the speed.

St. Ives Bay the scene of two Great White incidents?! © Richard Peirce.

During the swap I felt as if there was something circling the 3 of us in the water as we exchanged. I was eventually left alone after my friends had clambered on the 2-seater which I held steady. As they pulled away I had a sense of panic and drew my legs up to my knees, I can't explain why. I could see nothing but I felt something was not right, as I did so a long dark shape torpedoed where my feet had just been. About 9 feet behind where I was it broke the surface with a huge splash and circled back. It was steel dark grey, with a white underside, the dorsal fin broke the surface and a Great White – young, about 10-12 feet long turned back towards me. I think it may have been male but I couldn't be sure as it was so quick. My friends did not see or hear as they had roared off, and I had to turn and swim to the jet-ski which had floated a small distance away.

The shark and I both swam towards the ski, the shark went under the ski. I was terrified and got it running and pulled away, the shark swam almost underneath me for about 20ft, then disappeared.

I was fascinated, but not seeing it was more terrifying than seeing it and knowing where it was. We had a child in our group and I waved to get him off the jet-ski and on the boat. They thought I was having fun and waved back. In my concern I fell off, I never saw or felt the shark again and as our time was nearly up, I got back on and went over to my friends. I told the jet-ski guy who offered me a free hour which I did not accept. He told me it was probably a rare Sunfish, I explained I knew what I had seen, it had been terrifying and fascinating at the same time. I explained I was an experienced fishing person, I also explained I had been on the Prince Madog research vessel, and I knew that was no Sunfish. My friends thought I could have been mistaken. When we got to shore I tried to report the incident to the harbour master, but again no-one took it seriously.

A few weeks after there was a shark incident and there was speculation about a Great White. I think it was Padstow. What had surprised me was the incident reflected how controlled, patient, and curious the shark had been. I felt it had circled us for a long time and had waited until I was on my own, it was an opportunistic attack, by an inexperienced predator. Had it been older and wiser I don't think I would be here now. I have not discussed it much since then, as no-one took it seriously, but I believe there may be Great

24

Whites around our southern coasts. It was not a Mako, the head was more rounded and not so pointy." *Sally Houseago, Diss, Norfolk.*

PADSTOW, NORTH CORNWALL: AUGUST 1999

A leaked tip-off to the national press about the sighting of a large shark thought to be a Great White up the coast from Padstow near Crackington Haven resulted in a hysterical reaction and, at times, insulting scepticism. This combination made the fishing party involved dismayed that the story ever got out.

Mike Turner and Phil Britts, who were aboard the Blue Fox together with Phil's wife, Rhona, and others all saw a large shark about 37 metres (40 yards) away. The dorsal fin was clearly visible approaching them in a straight line as they were releasing a Soupfin Shark (Tope) which they had caught earlier.

The shark, estimated to be 4.6 metres (15 feet) long, passed the stern and rolled, revealing a clear white underside separated from the grey/ brown topside by a jagged line. It was visible for about a minute, having, at its nearest, come within 2 metres of the boat. Those on board believed that it had probably taken the Soupfin Shark (Tope) before disappearing.

A large black eye was noted and this, together with the colours and morphology described, are consistent with a Great White Shark. Mike had seen many Great Whites in South Africa and is adamant about the precision of his sighting. The others on board had seen a

25

The Blue Fox. © Blue Fox.

In summer 2002 I was summoned to view two extensively damaged seal carcasses in the Camel Estuary area, this is not one of them. © Unknown.

number of Porbeagles and Basking Sharks and ruled those out. It is noted that the proactive behaviour displayed in approaching the boat also fits the actions of a Great White Shark.

This incident and the two that follow all occurred in the same area at the same time which is typical of the credible sightings I have logged. Some commentators have treated these incidents in isolation, but when put together they make a far more compelling case. The reader will come across another good example of this in the North Uist incident of July 2005. The Quies Island incident which follows was also supported by other potential sightings at the same time in the same place.

CAMBEAK HEAD, NORTH CORNWALL: AUGUST 1999

The Blue Fox incident took place off Cambeak Head, and the following day there was a similar occurrence in exactly the same location. Paul Vincent was out with his friend Jason Coe fishing for Soupfin Shark (Tope) from his 5.2 metre (17 foot) dory, Blissful. Paul had hooked a Soupfin Shark (Tope), and was about to lift it aboard using his gaff hook when a very large shark appeared and bit off the bottom two thirds of the captured shark before swimming off. Paul estimates that it was at least as long as his boat. His full description was a match for the shark seen by those aboard the Blue Fox: the same grey/brown dorsal side, white ventral side, large triangular dorsal fin, black eye and unhurried, investigative behaviour.

TINTAGEL HEAD, NORTH CORNWALL: SEPTEMBER 1999

Less than two weeks after these incidents and about 12 miles away

The Quies Islands North Cornwall. © Richard Peirce.

The small seal colony on the Quies disappeared after the incident. © Richard Peirce.

28

near Tintagel Head, a lobster fisherman found a very large shark tangled up in his rope. He asked to remain anonymous – although his identity is known to me – and the whole incident I am about to describe was witnessed. When hauling in his pots there was what he thought was a snag in the line. It freed itself and then something hit the back of the davit. He went to look and saw the tail fin of a shark about 4.6 metres (15 feet) long. Because of its size, he thought it must be a Basking Shark.

Sharks cannot swim backwards and, if they land up in a rope, they often twist and become thoroughly entangled. Death follows unless they are freed quickly, and unfortunately that was the fate of this creature. As it had no commercial value, the only thing to do was to cut it loose. It was seen to have a slate grey topside and, as it was freed, it rolled showing a pure white underside. It also had what was described as a crescent-shaped mouth and triangular teeth. Basking Sharks and Porbeagles were both familiar to those on board and they were sure it was neither of those. At 4.6 metres (15 feet) what else could it have been? A Blue Shark or a Porbeagle? Very unlikely. A Mako? Again unlikely, and the colours and teeth as described don't fit.

So, three sharks each estimated to be the same size, each broadly fitting the same description and their sightings separated by only three weeks and 12 miles. Coincidence? Same shark? A Great White Shark?

QUIES ISLANDS, NORTH CORNWALL: JULY 2002

On a clear, almost windless day Brian Bate was laying his lobster pots to the northeast of the Quies Islands, when, suddenly, a large fish between 3.6 metres (12 feet) and 4.6 metres (15 feet) in length leapt completely out of the water with something in its mouth. Brian went to the spot and found a large spreading pool of blood with pieces of seal blubber floating in it. Seagulls were already feeding on the smaller pieces of blubber.

Leaping out of the water is called breaching and what Brian saw was a typical breaching attack, the size, body shape and colours precisely fitting a Great White Shark. When I showed him various photographs of breaching sharks, including those of Makos and Threshers, he identified the Great White. I suggested to him that it was a pity he hadn't retrieved one of the larger pieces of blubber in case a tooth might have been lodged in it, or the bite mark could have been identified. He told me that he didn't have a boathook and no sane person who had seen what he had would have started putting their hands in the water fishing around for bits of blubber!

If it wasn't a Great White, what else could it have been? For various reasons based on Brian's description, Blues, Porbeagles and Makos can be ruled out, which leaves a Killer Whale (Orca) as the only other possibility. Brian had seen many Orcas and was quite sure this hadn't been an Orca.

The triangular teeth of a Great White Shark and the sawing action of the jaws make dismemberment a typical occurrence, while this does not happen with the other sharks mentioned.

Two days after Brian Bate saw his 'breaching shark' kill a seal, a lone yachtsman sailed up the coast from Newquay to Padstow. He later recounted how a large shark followed in his wake for the greater part of his journey, and how he had sailed through the same water where Brian had seen the breaching attack. He is familiar with Basking Shark fins and is certain the shark that followed him was not one of those.

I went chumming in the Quies area with Brian two weeks after the seal predation and there were no seals to be seen where, normally, there is a small colony of between 15 and 20. The general area around Trevose Head, the Quies, the Camel Estuary and the offshore islands is home to several small population pockets of seals, but they did not return to the area until early October. I was alerted to two cases of washed-up seal remains, one in July before the Bates incident and the other in early August. Both carcasses consisted of only partial remains and both were extensively bird-pecked, making it impossible to determine how the seals died or learn anything from the wounds.

WESTERN ISLES, SCOTLAND: JULY 2003

To most people the idea of finding a Great White in Scottish waters would be no less improbable than finding the Loch Ness monster. Dr Simon Greenstreet was diving near Ullapool at the western edge of the Summer Isles, near Black Rock, on 4 July 2003. With him were his wife Wendy and two other divers in a 5.2 metre (17 ft.)

Shark in net off the north of Scotland. A Great White? © George Carter.

rigid inflatable boat. The Greenstreets had just finished their dive and the next pair were kitting up when a large fin was spotted some 28-36 metres (30–40 yards) away. The obvious thought was that it was a Basking Shark.

With the opportunity of swimming with a harmless shark in mind, Dr Greenstreet moved the boat closer. As soon as the engine started, the shark changed course and moved purposefully towards the boat. At this point, those on board still assumed it was a Basking Shark but, although nothing was said, doubts were creeping in.

When it was only 14 metres (15 yards) from the boat, the bulk of the shark was apparent. The distance from dorsal to tail fin was estimated at nearly three metres (9 feet). At that stage, the boat party realised this was no Basking Shark but it continued its approach, eventually swimming alongside only about half a metre away.

Those aboard judged the shark to be more than 4.6 metres (15 feet) in length. Dr Greenstreet has no specific shark interests but has seen enough Basking Sharks to know their particular characteristics. Unlike a Basking Shark, this one had a clearly defined white ventral side, a large solid broad-based triangular dorsal fin, a light grey dorsal side with clearly defined worn patches and smaller gills than the very large distinctive ones on a Basking Shark.

The description fits that of a Great White, as does its proactive behaviour in coming towards the boat when the engine was started. I believe that Dr Greenstreet and his party saw a Great White Shark.

NORTH EAST SCOTLAND: DECEMBER 2003

Five months after Dr Greenstreet's experience near Ullapool, a fisherman working off North East Scotland caught a large shark in his net. He did not wish to be named but I have interviewed him and others corroborate his story. What they all described was a large shark, 5.5 - 5.8 metres (18 - 19 feet) long with a large triangular dorsal fin snapping at small fish while it was trapped in the net. Teeth were observed but there is no accurate description of them, and the gills were not seen in sharp enough detail to be definitive. The fisherman was trying to work out how to release the shark when it managed to free itself.

The fisherman is not saying this was a Great White Shark, but he is adamant that it was not a Basking Shark. This does not leave many options and, as I had a photograph, I decided to send it to colleagues and seek their opinions. The image went to Great White Shark experts Ian Fergusson, Craig Ferreira, Jeremy Stafford-Deitsch, Leonard Compagno, Rolf Cyabaiski and others. Ian Fergusson and Leonard Compagno, two of the world's leading experts, collaborated in their reply and shared the opinion that, had I not told them the location was Scotland, but instead had said South Africa, southern Australia, or California, their first choice of identity would have been a Great White. However, because I had said "Scotland", they started thinking what else it might have been.

This is interesting. If I had simply said "I think this is a Great White; what do you think?" there is a good chance that two globally-renowned shark experts would have stuck to their original identification and the photograph would now be the first likely proof of a Great White in British waters.

NORTH UIST, SCOTLAND: JULY 2005

Modern languages school teacher Philip Harding, his colleague Alan and Alan's two teenage children were trolling for Pollock two miles south of Locheport at Aignish Point on the east coast of North Uist when Philip cut the engine to set up rods. At this point, a very large shark came up vertically beside the boat and had a good look at those on board before slowly diving and disappearing.

The features noticed were:

- a dark grey/bronzy dorsal side

- a pure white ventral side, so white that, for a split second, Philip thought the creature was an Orca before realising that it was a shark

- the shark was the length of the boat – 4.9 metres (16 feet)

- a very large girth and a solid (non-floppy), pointed, triangular dorsal fin

Philip and Alan are both very familiar with Basking Sharks and are quite adamant this was not one of those. However, the next day, just to be sure, Philip went to look at a freshly-dead Basking Shark caught in a net off Lochmaddy. Thereafter, he was able to confirm his initial impression that the morphology of the two sharks was markedly different in many respects.

Philip is certain that the animal he encountered was a Great White and, while he did not share this opinion with his boating colleagues on the day because he did not wish to alarm the youngsters, they have subsequently discussed the encounter and are all in agreement with his opinion.

A large seal population means an abundant food source. © *Jacqui Peirce.*

The big mystery is why, with apparently ideal conditions, we don't regularly get Great Whites in UK waters. © *Jacqui Peirce.*

Common and Grey Seals are abundant in that area and, to the west of North Uist, the Monach Islands have what is thought to be the largest seal colony in Europe. **N.B.** In September 2011 I spent 2 weeks on a shark search expedition based in Lochmaddy. The expedition attracted considerable local interest out of which came a report from a local fisherman of another sighting of what was thought to be a Great White Shark at the same time, and in the same place as Philip Harding's encounter. Sadly the witness, Angus John MacDonald had died in the meantime and so could not give me a firsthand account. However I interviewed his brother, Donald John MacDonald who was able to give me a very clear report of what his sibling had told him he saw. Angus was a sensible and highly experienced fisherman who would have known what he was looking at, and he was quite convinced that, like Philip Harding, he had seen a Great White Shark. The two sightings had happened within days of each other.

WESTERN ISLES SCOTLAND: JUNE 2007

Mathematician and marine scientist Jim Watson told me in June 2007 that he had been hearing regular reports of Great White Sharks in the Minch and Little Minch over the previous ten years. This fits with three of the more compelling accounts mentioned in this chapter. The Minch would be an ideal place for Great White Sharks: several seal colonies, and shoals of Haddock, Mackerel, Cod, Herring and Pollock provide an adequate food source, and the water temperatures (with summer highs of 16°C and winter lows of 7°C – 9°C) are comfortably within the tolerance range for these sharks for much of the year.

Jim has made more than 3000 dives and has worked extensively in the waters around the Hebrides off and on throughout his life. He accepts the possible presence of Great White Sharks in the Minch in an almost matter-of-fact manner.

I formed the impression that he would be more surprised by the suggestion that they were not there than they were there. Jim suggested I contact the Hebridean Whale and Dolphin Trust to see if it had any anecdotal or actual evidence of the presence of Great Whites. I spoke at length to Dr Peter Stevick and became interested when he offered to send me a picture of a large shark caught in the Minch some years ago and hitherto unidentified. The photograph turned out to be of a Mako, so there was no new evidence to add to my files.

SOUND OF HARRIS, SCOTLAND: LATE JUNE/EARLY JULY 2007

Film footage taken in the Sound of Harris on a mobile phone, possibly showing a shark attacking a seal, was sent to the Marine Conservation Society for comment in September 2007. Thereafter, it was passed onto the Shark Trust.

I have examined the footage as have the following other experts: Ian Fergusson, Jeremy Stafford-Deitsch, Leonard Compagno, Henry Mollet and Chris Fallows. I have also interviewed one of the eyewitnesses to the event.

Fergusson and Compagno both felt that the percentage likelihood in favour of the shark being a Great White was 60 per cent while there was a 40 per cent possibility of it being a Shortfin Mako. The other three felt it could be either but favoured a Shortfin Mako. My own view is that it was either a Shortfin Mako or, more probably, a Porbeagle.

The witness, Darren Steadwood, was at sea with two friends when extensive splashing in the water 18 metres away attracted their attention. They went to investigate and discovered a seal thrashing about on the surface. They were in a deep channel and could see it apparently being tossed about but didn't catch sight of a shark other than occasional glimpses of what might have been a fin. The video seems to show blood but Darren doesn't remember seeing any at the time.

Darren's friend recorded the incident on his mobile phone. The activity stopped and nothing happened for about 30 seconds and then a fin broke the surface between seven and nine metres away. They went to investigate as the shark swam away from them. Then it turned and swam towards the boat, going underneath it and then disappearing. There was no sign of the seal, or any seal remains, which may indicate that it had survived the attack and escaped if, indeed, it was an attack. My own opinion of the seal footage is that it is possibly two seals fighting or playing.

Darren estimated the length of the shark at three metres or just over, and recalls a stout body with a dark grey black dorsal (top) side. No gills were noticed. Darren did not get a view of the shark's underside and does not remember seeing its eyes. His initial

Basking Sharks are often reported as suspected Great Whites. © *Jacqui Peirce.*

Porbeagles are close relatives and are also often reported as possible Great Whites.
© *Dave Green.*

40

impression was not of the seal being attacked but of animals playing or maybe feeding, which is consistent with my opinion.

The footage shows a dorsal fin appearing from the left of the screen. The fin appears to have a slightly rounded apex with a straight down trailing edge and a curved forward edge. At this stage, the dorsal shape is certainly more representative of a Great White Shark than that of a Shortfin Mako. However, as the shark continues to move the footage becomes confusing because, at some angles, the apex of the dorsal appears more rounded. A caudal fin then comes into view and the shark at this point is swimming directly away from the photographer still moving across the screen from left to right.

There is still nothing conclusive and the next good 'side on' dorsal view shows a fin with a more rounded than pointed apex. The shark keeps swimming towards the right, disappears, then a caudal fin reappears followed by the dorsal. Thereafter, it turns around and starts swimming from the right to the left on an interception track with the boat.

The next good 'side on' of the dorsal once again seems to say "Great White Shark", with a more pointed apex and a straight-down, perhaps even slightly concave, trailing edge. The shark is swimming quite fast and possibly displaying excited behaviour. The seal has by now disappeared, so there is a possibility that the presence of seals out of sight below the water is influencing the shark's behaviour. The shark then swims right up to the vessel, possibly making contact with the hull, before swimming underneath, which is where the footage ends. The shark could have been a Great White Shark but, equally, it could have been a Shortfin Mako or, a Porbeagle.

It is interesting to note, that potential Great White Shark incidents that retain credibility after investigation are clustered in two areas: North Cornwall and the Western Isles (the Minch, Little Minch). There are only four possible Great White Shark incidents outside these areas that I am aware of – The Pentland Firth 'net capture' and escape in 2004, the Dartmouth seal incident of 1994, the possible spy hopping off Looe in the 1970's, and the 1965 Falmouth angling battle.

The Porbeagle is a first cousin of the Great White Shark. © Shark Conservation Society.

ST IVES, CORNWALL: JULY 2007

On Thursday 26 July, Dr Oliver Crimmen was shown a clip of amateur video by the Sun newspaper. It was taken on a video camcorder by Nick Fletcher while holidaying in St Ives. The film showed a small pod of Common Dolphins making their way along the coast and, at the end of the sequence, a creature is clearly seen to breach. Dr Crimmen was quoted as saying: "It's definitely predatory and definitely big. I can't rule out a Great White."

I, too, was asked to confirm the identity. But it was impossible because the film was not clear enough. All that could be seen for sure was that it was a fish somewhere between 2.4 metres (8 feet) and 3.6 metres (12 feet) long doing a half-to-three-quarters breach displaying a white ventral side. Given the close presence of dolphins, they must come into the reckoning as must Basking, Porbeagle and Mako Sharks.

If, as I do, you believe that Great Whites are occasional visitors to our shores then that possibility cannot be ruled out. However, saying they can't be ruled out is a long way from confirming that the image showed a Great White Shark, which is what the Sun inferred that I had done.

This sparked an extraordinary media frenzy and the Sun managed to string it out for a further eight days with all the other nationals and many regional papers joining in. Both the Monday and Tuesday editions of the paper carried front page pictures of Basking Shark's dorsal fins slicing through the waters off St Ives with various

This hoax photo on the front page of the Newquay Guardian in August 2007 marked the end of that year's St. Ives Great White fiasco.

44

'experts' identifying the fins as belonging to Great Whites. By Thursday, the Newquay Guardian's front page carried a picture of a Great White said to be taken off Towan Head, Newquay (See page 44). This was the first picture of a Great White to appear, but interest was waning and various other reports were hinting at doubts over where the photograph was taken. The photograph was later admitted to be a hoax.

During this time, the people of St Ives were, understandably, cashing in. Shark spotting boat trips were packed with excited tourists. Virtually everything that could float was taking to the sea to look for sharks. Cafes had maps of St Ives Bay on their walls with all the sightings marked. Shark ice creams, T-shirts and even shark-shaped pasties were produced to add to the fun and make the tills ring more frequently.

Nick Fletcher's original film clip had been forgotten by the time the story died. This was one of the most intense and long running shark sagas ever in the UK press, but was by no means based on compelling evidence.

Great Whites are truly magnificent creatures. I hope one day there will be a confirmed sighting in UK waters. © Richard Peirce.

CONCLUSIONS AND THE FUTURE

When and if a Great White Shark is confirmed in our waters we know that the tabloid media reaction will be one of hysteria. I wonder how the public will react? Have the tabloids done a Little Red Riding Hood and cried wolf, so often and so hysterically, that the public will react with a yawn and a "so what" attitude?

It would be both tragic and unfair if the first proven confirmed Great White Shark encounter involved an attack or a near attack on a human. None of us want to admit this too loudly but if, as I do, you believe we get the occasional vagrant visitor then you have to also believe that an attack is possible one day. The number of human water users increases every year, and this seems to be resulting in increased shark/human interaction in other places in the world, even though shark numbers are declining in most areas.

The wetsuit has changed everything and the UK is a perfect example. Surfers and other recreational water users are now active

Richard & Jacqui Peirce with the skippers and volunteers on the Sept. 2011 Western Isles expedition. © Unknown.

during the whole year, and more and more people are spending longer in the water. I live in north Cornwall, and if the surf is good then the late February sea temperatures don't put people off. I am often asked to rule out the possibility of an attack. I can't do this; I can only point to the facts which are:

- Great White numbers are depleted.

- There are no records of proven shark attacks in UK waters

- Even where there are known Great White Shark populations attacks are rare.

- Our marine conditions are already ideal for Great White Sharks, so don't let climate change and a probable rise in sea temperatures worry you. Other shark species may start appearing, but the Great White Shark enigma is why they are not already regular UK visitors or residents?

Whenever I have organised a large scale shark expedition in UK waters the media decide that the sole purpose of the expedition is to find a Great White Shark. In 2003 together with Craig Ferreira from South Africa I ran a three week shark search expedition off the north Cornish coast. Indeed we chummed all the places where I had records of credible Great White sightings or encounters, and had our fingers crossed, but we were embarked on a general shark search to see what would turn up, not a specific Great White hunt!

We had detailed plans for handling the news media which were working very well until a schoolgirl claimed to have spotted a Great White from a north Devon cliff! This event caused us to lose control and we never really regained it. The TV, newspapers, radio and glossy magazines all wanted in on the Great White Shark hunt.

Nearly a decade later I put together an expedition to the Western Isles. I had two aims and one hope. The aims were to see what sharks we could find, and to study marine conditions to see why they might not after all be suitable for Great Whites; the hope was that we might attract a V.I.P. visitor! I must be an eternal optimist because I planned to avoid the usual Great White media feeding frenzy, and to a large extent, we did. However this was only achieved through the careful release of information, and I am quite

Until there is conclusive proof the UK Great White Shark enigma will persist.
© *Harry Stone.*

sure that if I had said to a media interviewer that I had proof positive of the landing on the Hebrides of a green headed alien from Mars and had come to investigate, the interviewer would still have said "Yes, Richard but what about the Great White Shark"?

I had planned 14 days work with the Monach Islands as our primary target area, and the Sound of Harris and the east of North Uist as secondary objectives. Due to adverse weather conditions we only managed six days work at sea and never even got to the Monach Islands. Following this expedition we decided to abandon doing expeditions on pre-planned dates in British waters. Instead we will in future work reactively and put to sea when fair settled weather has set in.

The size of the world's Great White Shark population is not known, estimates vary between 3,000 – 5,000. In 2013 research published by the Dyer Island Conservation Trust indicated that the number of Great Whites using Gansbaai as an aggregation area was between 808 - 1,008. This was roughly half the previous local estimate, and had worrying implications for the global population. In California opinion is split with some believing the local population could be as low as 200 – 300, while others, like Chris Lowe of California State's Shark Lab, believe numbers are improving and it is a conservation success story.

Sharks have been on earth for hundreds of millions of years so man is the new kid on the block. Over exploitation, loss of habitat and many other factors are rapidly depleting what is left of the world's wildlife. The response of the conservation community is rather like doctors trying to treat advanced cancer with aspirin, sticking plasters and out of date drugs. At the end of 2014 a statement from the WWF and the Zoological Society of London said we had lost 50% of the world's wildlife in the last 40 years. Shark populations have been particularly hard hit due to the demand for fins for soup in the Far East. The Great White is listed as 'Vulnerable' by the International Union for Conservation and Nature.

I suspect that whether and when a Great White is confirmed in UK will depend on north Atlantic numbers making a recovery. It would be wonderful to see all sharks making a recovery, and a dream come true when we can add the Great White to the UK's list of marine mega fauna.

P.S. In July 2012 Scottish lobster fisherman, Jody McNeil, found a fossil Great White tooth caught in the rope attached to his lobster pot which he had hauled up from 80 fathoms (146m). Following this Dr. Charlie Underwood wrote an article in the Shark Trust magazine in which he examined the question of Great Whites in UK waters. This  excerpt is by kind permission of Dr. Underwood/The Shark Trust "About 4 million years ago, in the cool waters off Peru, the large populations of seals, dolphins and penguins formed a great reserve of potential prey for any shark able to live there. With the water too cold for *C. megalodon*, the gradual development of serrations in the teeth of *Cosmopolitodus* formed a smooth segue of that species into the first modern Great White Sharks. Within a short period this new predator had spread to cooler seas worldwide where it remained even after the extinctions of *C. megalodon* and *Cosmopolitodus* a (geologically) short time later.

Its large, triangular teeth are well known from sites in the Netherlands and elsewhere. More rarely associated with these are teeth of the true Great White Shark – close cousins co-occurring in northern Europe until a couple of million years ago. Despite the paucity of rocks of the correct age to contain fossils of these species in Britain, fossils of *Cosmopolitodus* do occur. Oddly these are most common in rocks deposited in East Anglia long after the species had become extinct.

The Gairloch White Shark...

So why are there no Great White Sharks in the North Sea and elsewhere around Britain now? Clearly the repeated advances of ice sheets and accompanying falls in sea level over the last million years would have driven the sharks south each time the ice advanced, but why did they not follow the ice back each time the climate warmed as they had elsewhere in the world? Or were they here but just unrecognised? A single tooth from a Scottish seabed throws up a fascinating insight but in some ways asks more questions than it answers. The tooth in question is from the anterior part of the upper jaw of an adult Great White Shark, and in-life wear to the tip suggests that this was an old, shed, tooth rather than coming from a shark carcass. So if the provenance of the tooth is genuine, and there is no reason to suggest otherwise, it proves that Great White Sharks once swam the waters of the Gairloch area and presumably elsewhere along the Atlantic seaboard. But when?

Six Feet of the

NADINE GORDI

My wife and I are not real farmers – not
bought our place, ten miles out of Johannes   .. .. main
roads, to change something in ourselves, I suppose; you seem to
rattle about so much within a marriage like ours. You long to hear
nothing but a deep, satisfying silence when you sound a marriage.
The farm hasn't managed that for us, of course, but it has done other
things, unexpected, illogical. Lerice, who I thought would retire
there in Chekhovian sadness for a month or two, and then leave the
place to the servants while she tried yet again to get a part she
wanted and become the actress she would like to be, has sunk into
the business of running the farm with all the serious intensity with
which she once imbued the shadows in a playwright's mind. I should
have given it up long ago if it had not been for her. Her hands, once
small and plain and well-kept – she was not the sort of actress who
wears red paint and diamond rings – are hard as a dog's pads.

I, of course, am there only in the evenings and at week-ends. I am
a partner in a luxury-travel agency, which is flourishing – needs to be,
as I tell Lerice, in order to carry on the farm. Still, though I know we
can't afford it, and though the sweetish smell of the fowls Lerice
breeds sickens me, so that I avoid going past their runs, the farm is
beautiful in a way I had almost forgotten – especially on a Sunday
morning when I get up and go out into the paddock and see not the
palm trees and fish pond and imitation-stone bird-bath of the
suburbs but white ducks on the dam, the lucerne field brilliant as
window-dresser's grass, and the little, stocky, mean-eyed bull,
lustful but bored, having his face tenderly licked by one of his ladies.
Lerice comes out with her hair uncombed, in her hand a stick
dripping with cattle-dip. She will stand and look dreamily for
a moment, the way she would pretend to look sometimes in those
plays. 'They'll mate to-morrow', she will say. 'This is their second
day. Look how she loves him, my little Napoleon.' So that when
people come out to see us on Sunday afternoon, I am likely to hear
myself saying, as I pour out the drinks, 'When I drive back home
from the city every day, past those rows of suburban houses, I
wonder how the devil we ever did stand it. . . Would you care to
look around?' And there I am, taking some pretty girl and her young

husband stumbling down to our river-bank, the girl catching her stockings on the mealie-stooks and stepping over cow-turds humming with jewel-green flies while she says, '. . . the *tensions* of the damned city. And you're near enough to get into town to a show, too! I think it's wonderful. Why, you've got it both ways!'

And for a moment I accept the triumph as if I *had* managed it – the impossibility that I've been trying for all my life – just as if the truth was that you could get it 'both ways', instead of finding yourself with not even one way or the other but a third, one you had not provided for at all.

But even in our saner moments, when I find Lerice's earthy enthusiasms just as irritating as I once found her histrionical ones, and she finds what she calls my 'jealousy' of her capacity for enthusiasm as big a proof of my inadequacy for her as a mate as ever it was, we do believe that we have at least honestly escaped those tensions peculiar to the city about which our visitors speak. When Johannesburg people speak of 'tension' they don't mean hurrying people in crowded streets, the struggle for money, or the general competitive character of city life. They mean the guns under the white men's pillows and the burglar bars on the white men's windows. They mean those strange moments on city pavements when a black man won't stand aside for a white man.

Out in the country, even ten miles out, life is better than that. In the country, there is a lingering remnant of the pretransitional stage; our relationship with the blacks is almost feudal. Wrong, I suppose, obsolete, but more comfortable all round. We have no burglar bars, no gun. Lerice's farm-boys have their wives and their piccaninis living with them on the land. They brew their sour beer without the fear of police raids. In fact, we've always rather prided ourselves that the poor devils have nothing much to fear, being with us; Lerice even keeps an eye on their children, with all the competence of a woman who has never had a child of her own, and she certainly doctors them all – children and adults – like babies whenever they happen to be sick.

It was because of this that we were not particularly startled one night last winter when the boy Albert came knocking at our window long after we had gone to bed. I wasn't in our bed but sleeping in the little dressing-room-cum-linen-room next door, because Lerice had annoyed me, and I didn't want to find myself softening toward her simply because of the sweet smell of the talcum powder on her flesh

4

after her bath. She came and woke me up. 'Albert says one of the boys is very sick', she said. 'I think you'd better go down and see. He wouldn't get us up at this hour for nothing.'

'What time is it?'

'What does it matter?' Lerice is maddeningly logical.

I got up awkwardly as she watched me – how is it I always feel a fool when I have deserted her bed? After all, I know from the way she never looks at me when she talks to me at breakfast the next day that she is hurt and humiliated at my not wanting her – and I went out, clumsy with sleep.

'Which of the boys is it?' I asked Albert as we followed the dance of my torch.

'He's too sick. Very sick, *Baas*', he said.

'But who? Franz?' I remembered Franz had had a bad cough for the past week.

Albert did not answer; he had given me the path, and was walking along beside me in the tall dead grass. When the light of the torch caught his face, I saw that he looked acutely embarrassed. 'What's this all about?' I said.

He lowered his head under the glance of the light. 'It's not me, *Baas*. I don't know. Petrus he send me.'

Irritated, I hurried him along to the huts. And there, on Petrus's iron bedstead, with its brick stilts, was a young man, dead. On his forehead there was still a light, cold sweat; his body was warm. The boys stood around as they do in the kitchen when it is discovered that someone has broken a dish – unco-operative, silent. Somebody's wife hung about in the shadows, her hands wrung together under her apron.

I had not seen a dead man since the war. This was very different. I felt like the others – extraneous, useless.

'What was the matter?' I asked.

The woman patted at her chest and shook her head to indicate the painful impossibility of breathing.

He must have died of pneumonia.

I turned to Petrus. 'Who was this boy? What was he doing here?' The light of a candle on the floor showed that Petrus was weeping. He followed me out the door.

When we were outside, in the dark, I waited for him to speak. But he didn't. 'Now come on, Petrus, you must tell me who this boy was. Was he a friend of yours?'

'He's my brother, *Baas*. He come from Rhodesia to look for work.'

The story startled Lerice and me a little. The young boy had walked down from Rhodesia to look for work in Johannesburg, had caught a chill from sleeping out along the way, and had lain ill in his brother Petrus's hut since his arrival three days before. Our boys had been frightened to ask us for help for him because we had not been intended ever to know of his presence. Rhodesian natives are barred from entering the Union unless they have a permit; the young man was an illegal immigrant. No doubt our boys had managed the whole thing successfully several times before; a number of relatives must have walked the seven or eight hundred miles from poverty to the paradise of zoot suits, police raids, and black slum townships that is their *Egoli*, City of Gold – the Bantu name for Johannesburg. It was merely a matter of getting such a man to lie low on our farm until a job could be found with someone who would be glad to take the risk of prosecution for employing an illegal immigrant in exchange for the services of someone as yet untainted by the city.

Well, this was one who would never get up again.

'You would think they would have felt they could tell *us*', said Lerice next morning. 'Once the man was ill. You would have thought at least —' When she is getting intense over something, she has a way of standing in the middle of a room as people do when they are shortly to leave on a journey, looking searchingly about her at the most familiar objects as if she had never seen them before. I had noticed that in Petrus's presence in the kitchen, earlier, she had the air of being almost offended with him, almost hurt.

In any case, I really haven't the time or inclination any more to go into everything in our life that I know Lerice, from those alarmed and pressing eyes of hers, would like us to go into. She is the kind of woman who doesn't mind if she looks plain, or odd; I don't suppose she would even care if she knew how strange she looks when her whole face is out of proportion with urgent uncertainty. I said, 'Now, I'm the one who'll have to do all the dirty work, I suppose.'

She was still staring at me, trying me out with those eyes – wasting her time, if she only knew.

'I'll have to notify the health authorities', I said calmly. 'They can't just cart him off and bury him. After all, we don't really know what he died of.'

She simply stood there, as if she had given up – simply ceased to see me at all.

I don't know when I've been so irritated. 'It might have been something contagious', I said. 'God knows?' There was no answer.

6

I am not enamoured of holding conversations with myself. I went out to shout to one of the boys to open the garage and get the car ready for my morning drive to town.

As I had expected, it turned out to be quite a business. I had to notify the police as well as the health authorities, and answer a lot of tedious questions: How was it I was ignorant of the boy's presence? If I did not supervise my native quarters, how did I know that that sort of thing didn't go on all the time? Et cetera, et cetera. And when I flared up and told them that so long as my natives did their work, I didn't think it my right or concern to poke my nose into their private lives, I got from the coarse, dull-witted police sergeant one of those looks that come not from any thinking process going on in the brain but from that faculty common to all who are possessed by the master-race theory – a look of insanely inane certainty. He grinned at me with a mixture of scorn and delight at my stupidity.

Then I had to explain to Petrus why the health authorities had to take away the body for a post-mortem – and, in fact, what a post-mortem was. When I telephoned the health department some days later to find out the result, I was told the cause of death was, as we had thought, pneumonia, and that the body had been suitably disposed of. I went out to where Petrus was mixing a mash for the fowls and told him that it was all right, there would be no trouble; his brother had died from that pain in his chest. Petrus put down the paraffin tin and said, 'When can we go to fetch him, *Baas*?'

'To fetch him?'

'Will the *Baas* please ask them when we must come?'

I went back inside and called Lerice, all over the house. She came down the stairs from the spare bedrooms, and I said, '*Now* what am I going to do? When I told Petrus, he just asked calmly when they could go and fetch the body. They think they're going to bury him themselves.'

'Well go back and tell him', said Lerice. 'You must tell him. Why didn't you tell him then?'

When I found Petrus again, he looked up politely. 'Look, Petrus', I said. 'You can't go to fetch your brother. They've done it already – they've *buried* him, you understand?'

'Where?' he said slowly, dully, as if he thought that perhaps he was getting this wrong.

'You see, he was a stranger. They knew he wasn't from here, and they didn't know he had some of his people here, so they thought

7

they must bury him.' It was difficult to make a pauper's grave sound like a privilege.

'Please, *Baas*, the *Baas* must ask them?' But he did not mean that he wanted to know the burial-place. He simply ignored the incomprehensible machinery I told him had set to work on his dead brother; he wanted the brother back.

'But Petrus', I said, 'how can I? Your brother is buried already. I can't ask them now.'

'Oh *Baas!*' he said. He stood with his bran-smeared hands uncurled at his sides, one corner of his mouth twitching.

'Good God, Petrus, they won't listen to me! They can't, anyway. I'm sorry, but I can't do it. You understand?'

He just kept on looking at me, out of his knowledge that white men have everything, can do anything; if they don't, it is because they won't.

And then, at dinner Lerice started. 'You could at least phone', she said.

'*Christ*, what d'you think I am? Am I supposed to bring the dead back to life?'

But I could not exaggerate my way out of this ridiculous responsibility that had been thrust on me. 'Phone them up', she went on. 'And at least you'll be able to tell him you've done it and they've explained that it's impossible.'

She disappeared somewhere into the kitchen quarters after coffee. A little later she came back to tell me, 'The old father's coming down from Rhodesia to be at the funeral. He's got a permit and he's already on his way.'

Unfortunately, it was not impossible to get the body back. The authorities said that it was somewhat irregular, but that since the hygiene conditions had been fulfilled, they could not refuse permission for exhumation. I found out that, with the undertaker's charges, it would cost twenty pounds. Ah, I thought, that settles it. On five pounds a month, Petrus won't have twenty pounds – and just as well, since it couldn't do the dead any good. Certainly I should not offer it to him myself. Twenty pounds – or anything else within reason, for that matter – I would have spent without grudging it on doctors or medicines that might have helped the boy when he was alive. Once he was dead, I had no intention of encouraging Petrus to throw away, on a gesture, more than he spent to clothe his whole family in a year.

When I told him, in the kitchen that night, he said, 'Twenty pounds?'

I said, 'Yes, that's right, twenty pounds.'

For a moment, I had the feeling, from the look on his face, that he was calculating. But when he spoke again I thought I must have imagined it. 'We must pay twenty pounds!' he said in the far-away voice in which a person speaks of something so unattainable that it does not bear thinking about.

'All right, Petrus', I said in dismissal, and went back to the living-room.

The next morning before I went to town, Petrus asked to see me. 'Please *Baas*', he said, awkwardly handling me a bundle of notes. They're so seldom on the giving rather than the receiving side, poor devils, that they don't really know how to hand money to a white man. There it was, the twenty pounds, in ones and halves, some creased and folded until they were soft as dirty rags, others smooth and fairly new – Franz's money, I suppose, and Albert's, and Dora the cook's, and Jacob the gardener's, and God knows who else's besides, from all the farms and small holdings round about. I took it in irritation more than in astonishment, really – irritation at the waste, the uselessness of this sacrifice by people so poor. Just like the poor everywhere, I thought, who stint themselves the decencies of life in order to ensure themselves the decencies of death. So incomprehensible to people like Lerice and me, who regard life as something to be spent extravagantly and, if we think about death at all, regard it as the final bankruptcy.

The servants don't work on Saturday afternoon anyway, so it was a good day for the funeral. Petrus and his father had borrowed our donkey-cart to fetch the coffin from the city, where, Petrus told Lerice on their return, everything was 'nice' – the coffin waiting for them, already sealed up to save them from what must have been a rather unpleasant sight after two weeks' interment. (It had taken all that time for the authorities and the undertaker to make the final arrangements for moving the body.) All morning, the coffin lay in Petrus's hut, awaiting the trip to the little old burial-ground, just outside the eastern boundary of our farm, that was a relic of the days when this was a real farming district rather than a fashionable rural estate. It was pure chance that I happened to be down there near the fence when the procession came past; once again Lerice had forgotten her promise to me and had made the house uninhabitable on a Saturday afternoon. I had come home and been

9

infuriated to find her in a pair of filthy old slacks and with her hair uncombed since the night before, having all the varnish scraped off the living-room floor, if you please. So I had taken my No. 8 iron and gone off to practise my approach shots. In my annoyance I had forgotten about the funeral, and was reminded only when I saw the procession coming up the path along the outside of the fence toward me; from where I was standing, you can see the graves quite clearly, and that day the sun glinted on bits of broken pottery, a lopsided homemade cross, and jam-jars brown with rain-water and dead flowers.

I felt a little awkward, and did not know whether to go on hitting my golf ball or stop at least until the whole gathering was decently past. The donkey-cart creaks and screeches with every revolution of the wheels and it came along in a slow halting fashion somehow peculiarly suited to the two donkeys who drew it, their little pot-bellies rubbed and rough, their heads sunk beneath the shafts, and their ears flattened back with an air submissive and downcast; peculiarly suited, too, to the group of men and women who came along slowly behind. The patient ass. Watching, I thought, you can see now why the creature became a Biblical symbol. Then the procession drew level with me and stopped, so I had to put down my club. The coffin was taken down off the cart – it was a shiny, yellow-varnished wood, like cheap furniture – and the donkeys twitched their ears against the flies. Petrus, Franz, Albert and the old father from Rhodesia hoisted it on their shoulders and the procession moved on, on foot. It was really a very awkward moment. I stood there rather foolishly at the fence, quite still, and slowly they filed past, not looking up, the four men bent beneath the shiny wooden box, and the straggling troop of mourners. All of them were servants or neighbours' servants whom I knew as casual, easygoing gossipers about our lands or kitchen. I heard the old man's breathing.

I had just bent to pick up my club again when there was a sort of jar in the flowing solemnity of their processional mood; I felt it at once, like a wave of heat along the air, or one of those sudden currents of cold catching at your legs in a placid stream. The old man's voice was muttering something; and they bumped into one another, some pressing to go on, others hissing at them to be still. I could see that they were embarrassed, but they could not ignore the voice; it was much the way that the mumblings of a prophet, though not clear at first, arrest the mind. The corner of the coffin the old man carried was sagging at an angle; he seemed to be trying to get out

10

from under the weight of it. Now Petrus expostulated with him.

The little boy who had been left to watch the donkeys dropped the reins and ran to see. I don't know why – unless it was for the same reason people crowd round someone who has fainted in a cinema – but I parted the wires of the fence and went through, after him.

Petrus lifted his eyes to me – to anybody – with distress and horror. The old man from Rhodesia had let go of the coffin entirely, and the three others, unable to support it on their own, had laid it on the ground, in the pathway. Already there was a film of dust lightly wavering up its shiny sides. I did not understand what the old man was saying; I hesitated to interfere. But now the whole seething group turned on my silence. The old man himself came over to me, with his hands outspread and shaking, and spoke directly to me, saying something that I could tell from the tone, without understanding the words, was shocking and extraordinary.

'What is it, Petrus? What's wrong?' I appealed.

Petrus threw up his hands, bowed his head in a series of hysterical shakes, then thrust his face up at me suddenly.

'He says, "My son was not so heavy".'

Silence. I could hear the old man breathing; he kept his mouth a little open as old people do.

'My son was young and thin', he said, at last, in English.

Again silence. Then babble broke out. The old man thundered against everybody; his teeth were yellowed and few, and he had one of those fine, grizzled, sweeping moustaches that one doesn't often see nowadays, which must have been grown in emulation of early Empire builders. It seemed to frame all his utterances with a special validity, perhaps merely because it was the symbol of the traditional wisdom of age – an idea so fearfully rooted that it carries still something awesome beyond reason. He shocked them; they thought he was mad, but they had to listen to him. With his own hands he began to prise the lid off the coffin and three of the men came forward to help him. Then he sat down on the ground; very old, very weak, and unable to speak, he merely lifted a trembling hand toward what was there. He abdicated, he handed it over to them; he was no good any more.

They crowded round to look (and so did I), and now they forgot the nature of this surprise and the occasion of grief to which it belonged, and for a few minutes were carried up in the astonishment of the surprise itself. They gasped and flared noisily with excitement. I even noticed the little boy who had held the donkeys jumping up and down, almost weeping with rage because the backs of the grown-ups crowded him out of his view.

In the coffin was someone no one had ever seen before: a heavily built, rather light-skinned native with a neatly stitched scar on his forehead – perhaps from a blow in a brawl that had also dealt him some other, slower-working injury which had killed him.

I wrangled with the authorities for a week over that body. I had the feeling that they were shocked, in a laconic fashion, by their own mistake, but that in the confusion of their anonymous dead they were helpless to put it right. They said to me, 'We are trying to find out', and 'We are still making enquiries.' It was as if at any moment they might conduct me into their mortuary and say, 'There! Lift up the sheets; look for him – your poultry boy's brother. There are so many black faces – surely one will do?'

And every evening when I got home Petrus was waiting in the kitchen. 'Well, they're trying. They're still looking. The *Baas* is seeing to it for you, Petrus', I would tell him. 'God, half the time I should be in the office I'm driving around the back end of town chasing after this affair', I added aside, to Lerice, one night.

She and Petrus both kept their eyes turned on me as I spoke, and, oddly, for those moments they looked exactly alike, though it sounds impossible: my wife, with her high, white forehead and her attenuated Englishwoman's body, and the poultry boy, with his horny bare feet below khaki trousers tied at the knee with string and the peculiar rankness of his nervous sweat coming from his skin.

'What makes you so indignant, so determined about this now?' said Lerice suddenly.

I stared at her. 'It's a matter of principle. Why should they get away with a swindle? It's time these officials had a jolt from someone who'll bother to take the trouble.'

She said, 'Oh.' And as Petrus slowly opened the kitchen door to leave, sensing that the talk had gone beyond him, she turned away too.

I continued to pass on assurances to Petrus every evening, but although what I said was the same, and the voice in which I said it was the same, every evening it sounded weaker. At last, it became clear that we would never get Petrus's brother back, because nobody really knew where he was. Somewhere in a graveyard as uniform as a housing scheme, somewhere under a number that didn't belong to him, or in the medical school, perhaps, laboriously reduced to layers of muscles and strings of nerves? Goodness knows. He had no identity in this world anyway.

It was only then, and in a voice of shame, that Petrus asked me to try and get the money back.

'From the way he asks, you'd think he was robbing his dead brother', I said to Lerice later. But as I've said, Lerice had got so intense about this business that she couldn't even appreciate a little ironic smile.

I tried to get the money; Lerice tried. We both telephoned and wrote and argued, but nothing came of it. It appeared that the main expense had been the undertaker, and, after all, he had done his job. So the whole thing was a complete waste, even more of a waste for the poor devils than I had thought it would be.

The old man from Rhodesia was about Lerice's father's size, so she gave him one of her father's old suits and he went back home rather better off, for the winter, than he had come.